Frisky was a little lamb.

She lived in a farmyard with a cat,

a horse, three ducks and six hens.

Frisky was always getting up to mischief.

One day Frisky was hiding from the cat.

'I can't see Frisky anywhere,' said the cat.

So the cat went off to look for Frisky.

1

The cat went in to the stable.

Frisky went in to the stable too.

The cat went up to the horse.
'Is Frisky in here?' said the cat.

'No,' said the horse.
'Frisky is not here.'

The cat went in to the shed.
The horse went in to the shed.

Frisky went in to the shed too.

The cat went up to the hens.
'Is Frisky in here?' said the cat.

'No,' said the hens.
'Frisky is not here.'

'I can't see Frisky,' said the cat.
'I can't see Frisky,'
said the horse.

'We can't see Frisky,'
said the hens.